JOSEPH HAYDN

SYMPHONY NO. 45

F$^\sharp$ minor/fis-Moll/Fa$^\sharp$ mineur
Hob. I: 45
"Farewell"
„Abschieds-Sinfonie"

Edited by/Herausgegeben von
Ernst Praetorius

T0081265

Ernst Eulenburg Ltd

London · Mainz · Madrid · New York · Paris · Prague · Tokyo · Toronto · Zürich

Haydn, Symphony No. 45, F sharp minor ("Farewell")

The following report about the origin of this work (called "Abschieds-Symphonie" in Germany, "Symphonie des Adieux" in France, "Farewell Symphony" or "Candle Overture" in England) seems to be auhentic.

The orchestra of Prince Esterhàzy, under Haydn's directorship (1761-1790) consisted in the winter of 1772 of 16 members (6 Violins, each 1 Viola, Cello, Double Bass, Bassoon, 2 Oboes, 4 Horns). Lack of space at the castle of Esterház and the assembly of numerous artists, together with their families, involved difficulties, which the Prince tried to remedy by notifying his musicians that he did not want to see their families for at least 24 hours. Exempted from this prohibition were the families of Haydn, the two Kammersänger Fribert and Dichtler and the first Violinist Tomasini. During the Prince's absence the musicians were allowed to meet their families at Eisenstadt. In 1772 the Prince stayed at the castle for an unusually long period. The musicians, anxious as regards their family life, applied to "Papa Haydn" for his help. Personal or written applications to the Prince would have been useless. Haydn found a happy solution. At the next Court concert the première of his new symphony took place.

The key in which the work was written was unusual. The first movement created a resolute and virile atmosphere, while the second breathed softness and mildness, and seemed almost to implore leniency or consideration (Violins con Sordino). The normal ease of the Menuett, however, did not come through in the third movement. The fourth displayed spasmodic efforts to create a merry mood, but after a halt on the dominant (bar 150) instead of the usual f sharp major or minor continuation, an Adagio appeared (A major). In bar 31 the Oboe I and Horn II stopped playing, packed up their instruments, blew out their candles and disappeared. Eleven bars later the Bassoon, after twice reiterating the initial bars of the first subject, left in silence. After a further seven bars Horn I and Oboe II followed. The Cellist and Double Bass parted company, the Bass player departed shortly after, followed after 10 bars by the Cellist, after a further 18 bars the Violins III and IV departed. Nine bars later only one first and one second Violin remained. Painfully and fading away they finished the Symphony. The last candles were extinguished and Haydn followed the musicians in silence. Prince Nikolaus, however, stopped him, saying: " I have realised your intention; the musicians are longing for home. Well, to-morrow we pack up.'

This edition was undertaken from the complete edition (Breitkopf & Härtel, Serie I, Vol. IV, 1933) and the orchestral parts (Symphonie à moyen orchestre composée par J. H. chez A. Kühnel, Bureau de Musique à Leipzig, 1809) in the possession of Herr A. van Hoboken, Vienna, to whom we are indebted for this favour.

ERNEST PRAETORIUS

Revisionsbericht

Autograph der Partitur im Archiv des Fürsten Esterhazi (Eisenstadt, jetzt Budapest). 64 Seiten in Hochfolio. Überschrift: „Sinfonia in Fis minore. In Nomine Domini di me Giuseppe Haydn. 772." I. Satz: Seite 1—17, II. Satz: Seite 21 bis 28, III. Satz: Seite 29—32, IV. Satz: Seite 33—60. Seite 18—20, 61—64 leer, am Schluß „Laus Deo".

Von den Berichten über die Entstehungsgeschichte der Sinfonie (in Deutschland „Abschiedssinfonie", in Frankreich „Symphony des Adieux", in England „Farewell-symphony" oder „Candle overture" genannt) dürfte folgender authentisch sein.

Die Kapelle des Fürsten Nicolaus Esterhazi, die Haydn von 1761—1790 künstlerisch betreute, bestand im Winter des Jahres 1772 aus 16 Mitgliedern (6 Violinen, 1 Viola, 1 Violoncello, 1 Contrabaß, 2 Oboen, 4 Hörner. Der Raummangel auf Schloß Esterház und das Zusammenleben zahlreicher Künstlerfamilien führte zu Schwierigkeiten, denen der Fürst im Januar 1772 dadurch abzuhelfen suchte, daß er seinen Musikern mitteilen ließ, er wolle „künftighin ihre Weiber und Kinder nicht einmal auf 24 Stunden in E. sehen". Ausgenommen von diesem Verbot blieben die Familien des Kapellmeisters Haydn, der Kammersänger Fribert und Dichter sowie des I. Violinisten Tomasini. Nur während der Abwesenheit des Fürsten durften die Musiker von E. nach Eisenstadt zum Besuch ihrer dort stationierten Familien. Im Jahre 1772 blieb Fürst E. ungewöhnlich lange auf Schloß E. Die um ihr Familienleben gebrachten Musiker wandten sich hilfeflehend an „Papa Haydn". Persönliche oder schriftliche Gesuche beim Fürsten hätten nur einen Heiterkeitserfolg gebracht. Haydn fand die geniale Lösung. In dem nächsten Hofkonzert fand die Uraufführung seiner neuen Sinfonie statt.

Schon die Tonart war ungewöhnlich. Der I. Satz (Allegro assai $\frac{3}{4}$) zeigte eine entschlossene und mannhafte Haltung, während die II. Satz (Adagio A-dur, $\frac{3}{8}$) Weichheit und Milde bewies und auch um solche zu bitten schien. (Violinen con sordino.) Die sonst übliche Sorglosigkeit eines Menuetts kommt im III. Satz nicht recht zum Durchbruch. Der IV. Satz (Presto fis-moll alla breve) bemüht sich fast ein wenig krampfhaft, eine fröhliche Stimmung durchzusetzen; nach einem Halt auf der Dominante (Takt 150) tritt anstatt der zu erwartenden Fis-dur- oder fis-moll-Fortsetzung ein Adagio (A-dur $\frac{3}{8}$) auf. Im 31. Takt beenden Oboe I und Horn II ihr Spiel, die Künstler packen ihre Instrumente ein und verschwinden. 11 Takte später bringt das Fagott gerade noch zweimal die Anfangstakte des I. Motivs, um sich dann stillschweigend zu verabschieden. Nach weiteren 7 Takten folgen Horn I und Oboe II. Violoncello und Contrabaß trennen sich, dieser geht bald darauf ab. Ihm folgt nach 10 Takten das Violoncello, nach 18 Takten die Violine III und IV. 9 Takte später ist von dem gesamten Orchester nur noch eine I. und II. Violine übrig geblieben. Schmerzlich und leise ersterbend (con sordino) beenden sie die Sinfonie. Die letzten Lichter sind verloschen, auch Haydn will seinen Musikern stillschweigend folgen. Fürst Nicolaus hält ihn auf: „Ich habe Ihre Absicht wohl durchschaut, die Musiker sehnen sich nach Hause — nun gut — morgen packen wir ein".

Die Revision erfolgte nach der Gesamtausgabe (Breitkopf & Härtel, Serie I, Band IV, 1933) und Orchesterstimmen (Symphonie à moyen orchestre composée par J. H. chez A. Kühnel, Bureau de Musique à Leipzig 1809), aus dem Besitz des Herrn A. van Hoboken-Wien, dem wir zu Dank verpflichtet sind.

Ernst Praetorius

SYMPHONY No.45

I

Allegro assai

Joseph Haydn
1732-1809

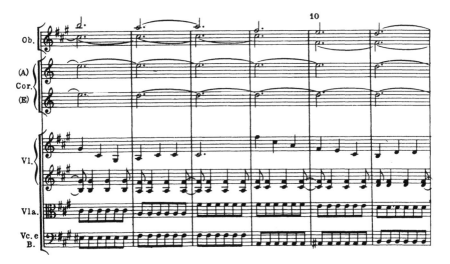

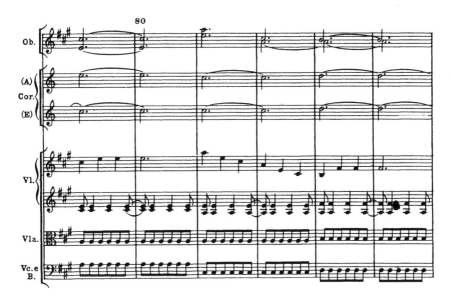

150

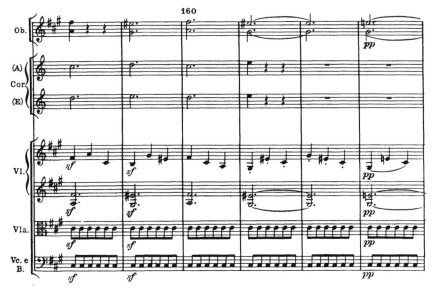

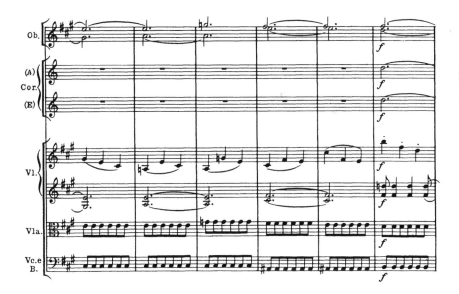

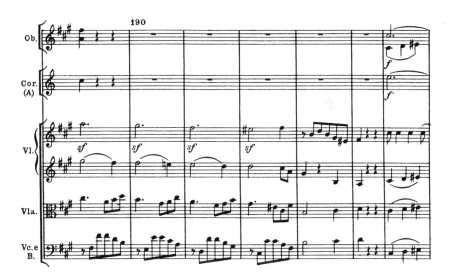

II

Adagio

19

22

III

60

70

Menuet da capo

IV

Finale
Presto

28

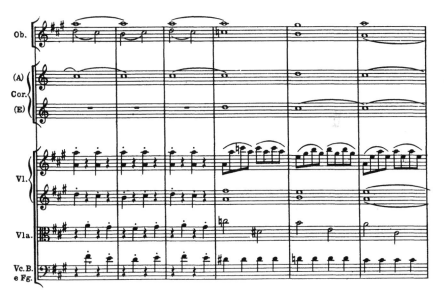

30

34

38

40

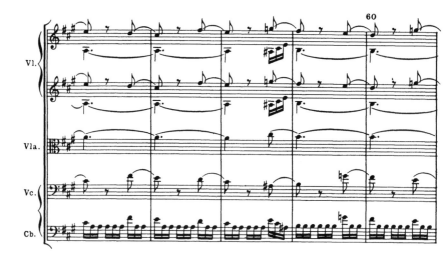

con sordino

con sordino